OUT OF LINE

BY **ALEX FRANCIS**

ILLUSTRATED BY **ALAN BROWN**

GRAFFIX BOOKS

Walkthrough

Read this first - or turn the page to go straight to the story!

The Characters

The characters in this story are made up of two teams. Which team will win the match?

The Teams

The Red Rebels

The Red Rebels are the away team. They are not very friendly.

The Crazy Cubs

Kade

Kade is one of the strikers of the Crazy Cubs. He is quick to act, but needs to think things through sometimes.

Jamal

Jamal is the captain of the Crazy Cub football team. He is quiet and looks after his teammates.

Elli

Elli is one of the defenders of the Crazy Cubs. She is good at getting everyone in line.

Tom

Tom is another defender of the Crazy Cubs. He is shy but will do anything to stand up for his friends.

The game begins.

Both teams play their hardest.

With only a few minutes left it is neck and neck.

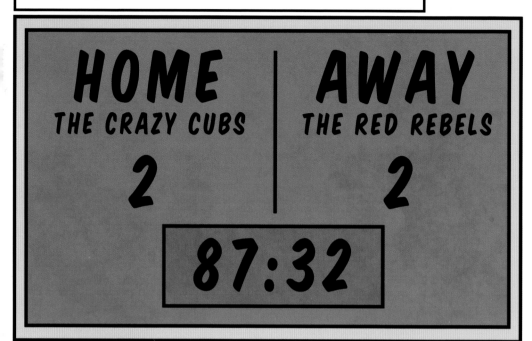

Jamal takes the free kick.

THE END.

Extra Time...

Answer the questions below. Each correct answer gains you points. Are you a Trainee or a Manager?

1 *Multiple Choice:*
What happens to the Crazy Cubs' ball?
a) It is ripped
b) It is lost in a garden
c) It is taken by another team

1pt

2 *Multiple Choice:*
Whose window is broken?
a) Mr Rogers
b) Kade
c) The referee

1pt

3 Who do the Crazy Cubs play the day after the window is broken?

2pts

4 *Fill in the sentence:*
Jamal takes the free _____ .

3pts

6 *Multiple Choice:*
At the end, why do you think the Crazy Cubs let the other team play with them? **1pt**
a) They want a rematch
b) The other boys said sorry
c) Their parents told them to

Answers on the next page. Every correct answer earns points (pts) Which level are you?

Level:

0 - 1pts = Trainee
2 - 4pts = Substitute
5 - 7pts = Striker
8 - 9pts = Head Coach
10pts = Manager

Explore...

Think about the following:

- How did the Crazy Cubs feel when Mr Rogers told them off?

- What else could the other team have done to make it up to the Crazy Cubs?

- How do you think the Crazy Cubs felt when the other team said sorry?

Other Titles

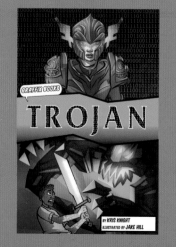